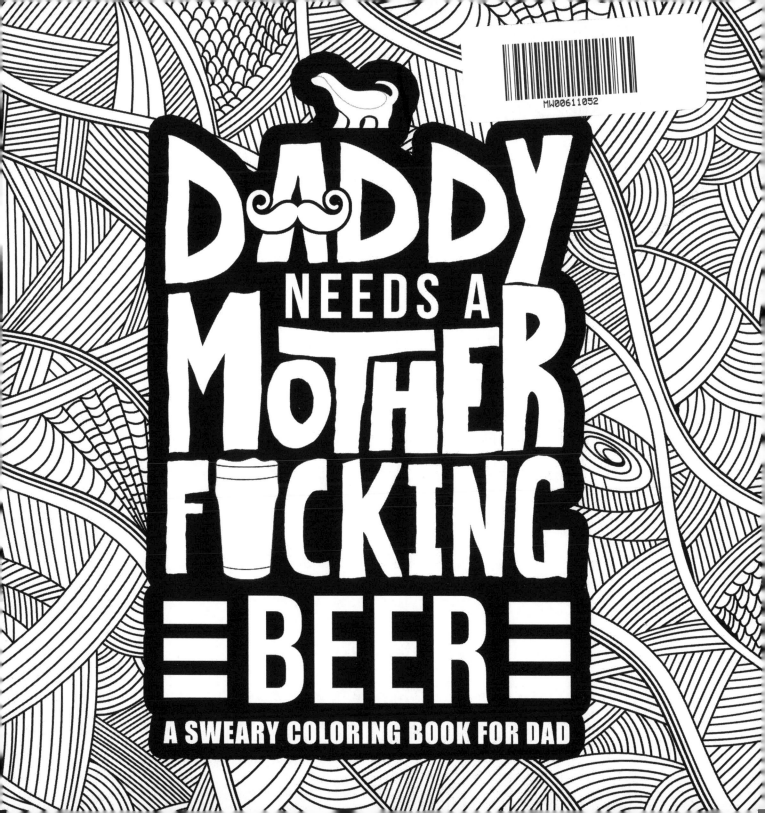

Want free goodies?
Email us at freebies@honeybadgercoloring.com

@honeybadgercoloring

Honey Badger Coloring

Shop our other books at
www.honeybadgercoloring.com

Wholesale distribution through Ingram Content Group
www.ingramcontent.com/publishers/distribution/wholesale

For questions and customer service, email us at
support@honeybadgercoloring.com

# FREE PDF DOWNLOAD

## OF THIS BOOK

DILF

P F P
bomb

I SWEAR BECAUSE I CARE

DOWNLOAD CODE:

DAD3963

www.honeybadgercoloring.com/dadswears

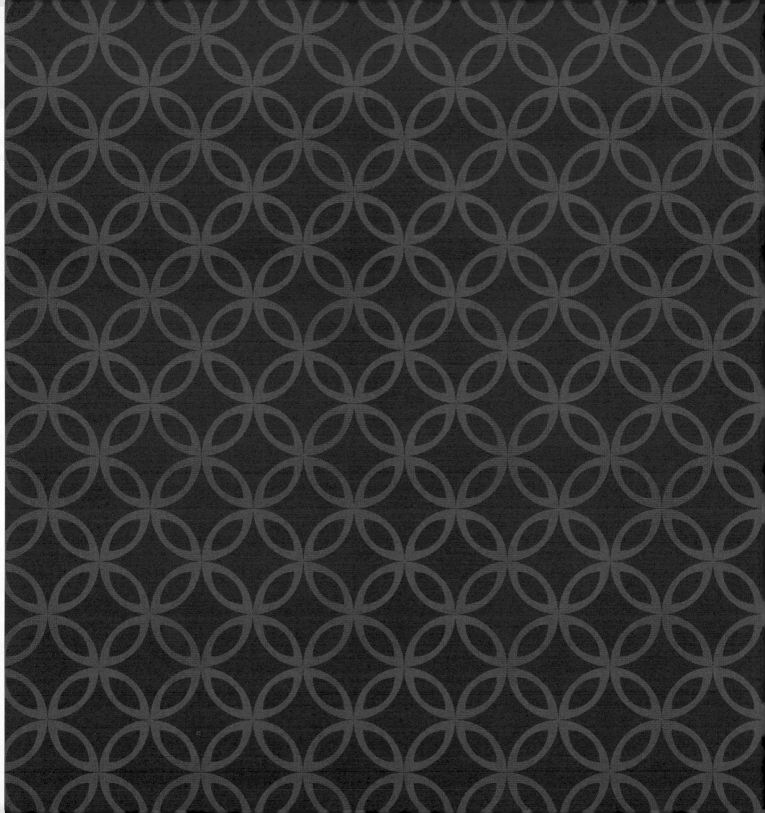

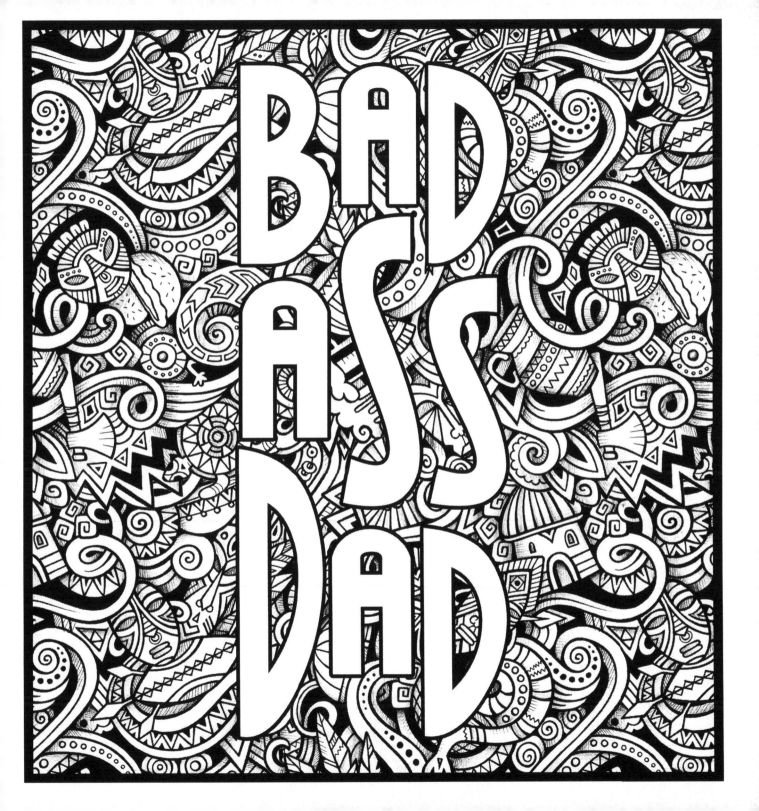

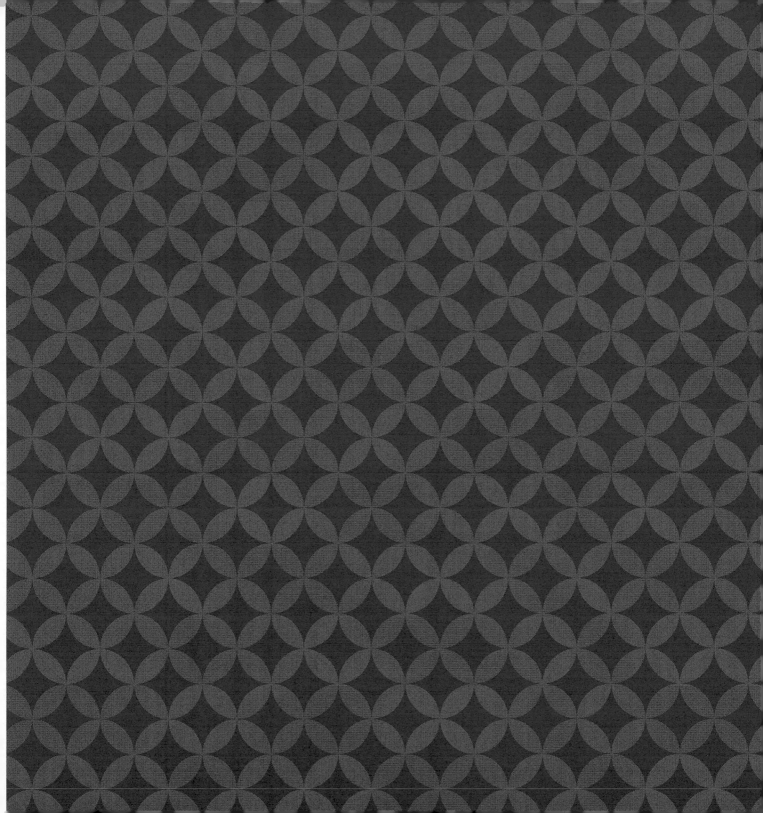

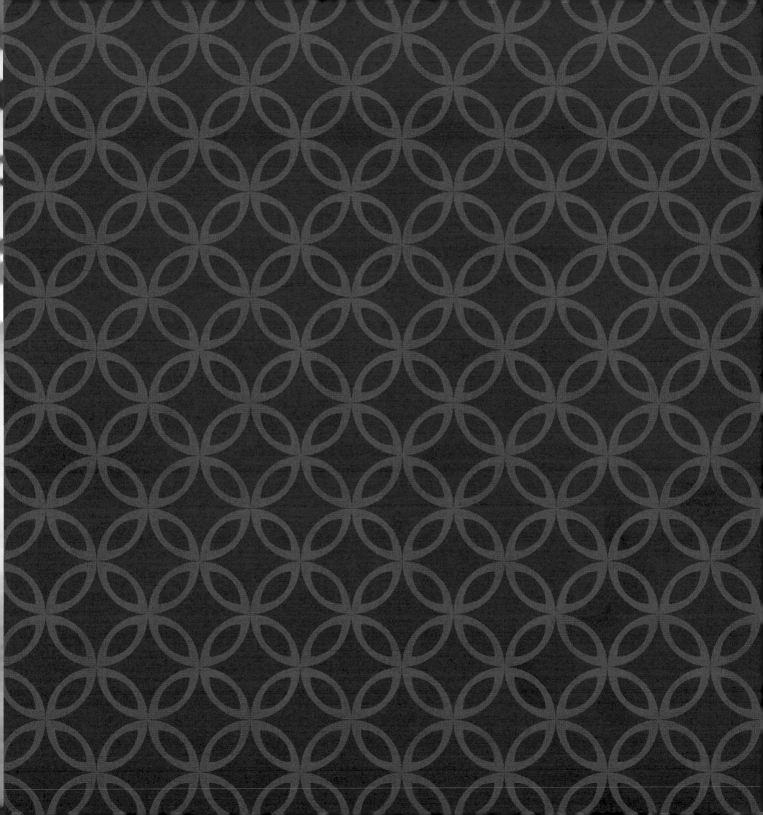

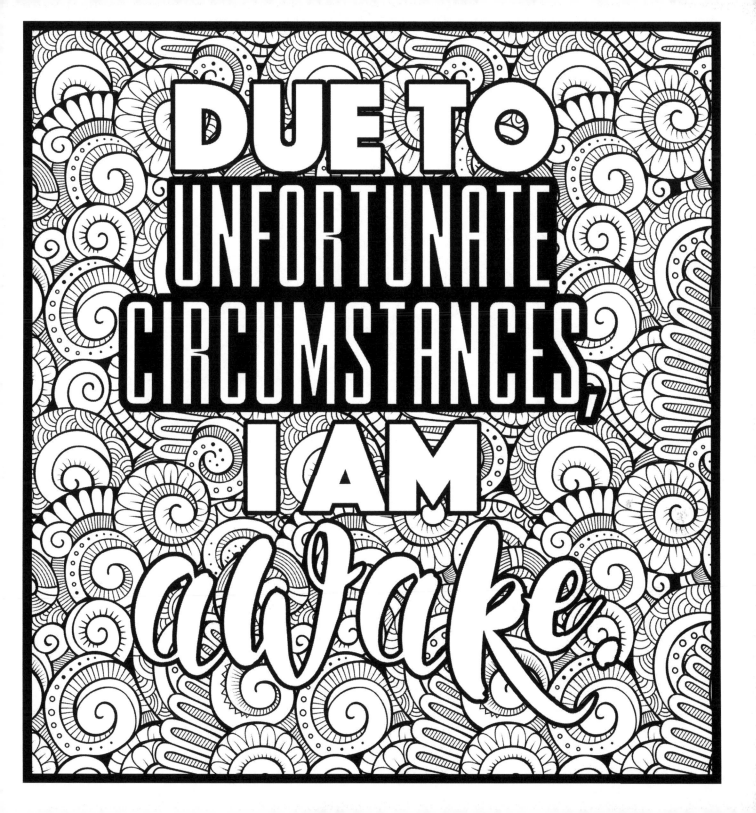

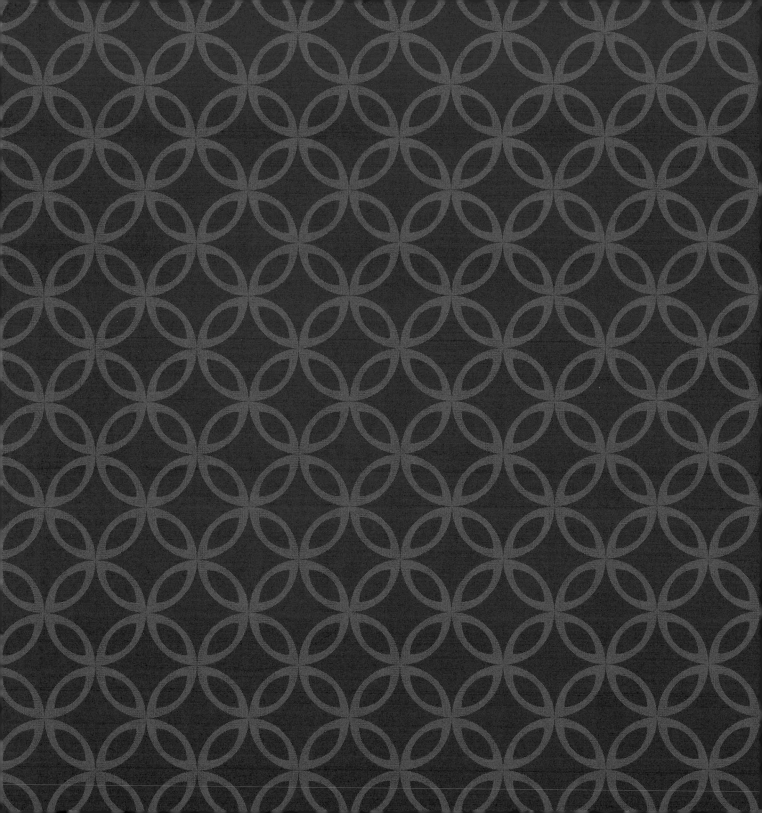

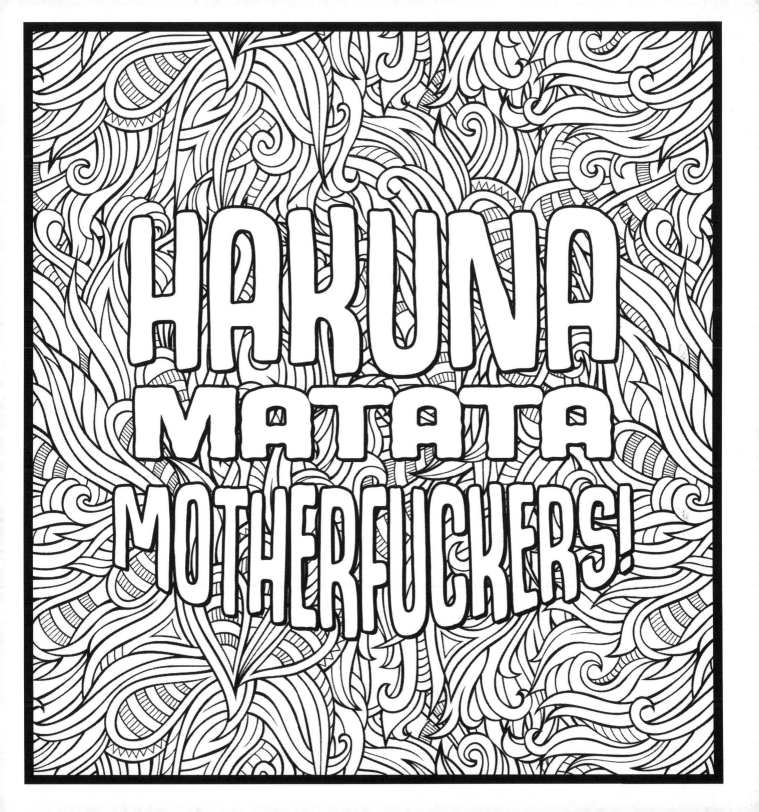

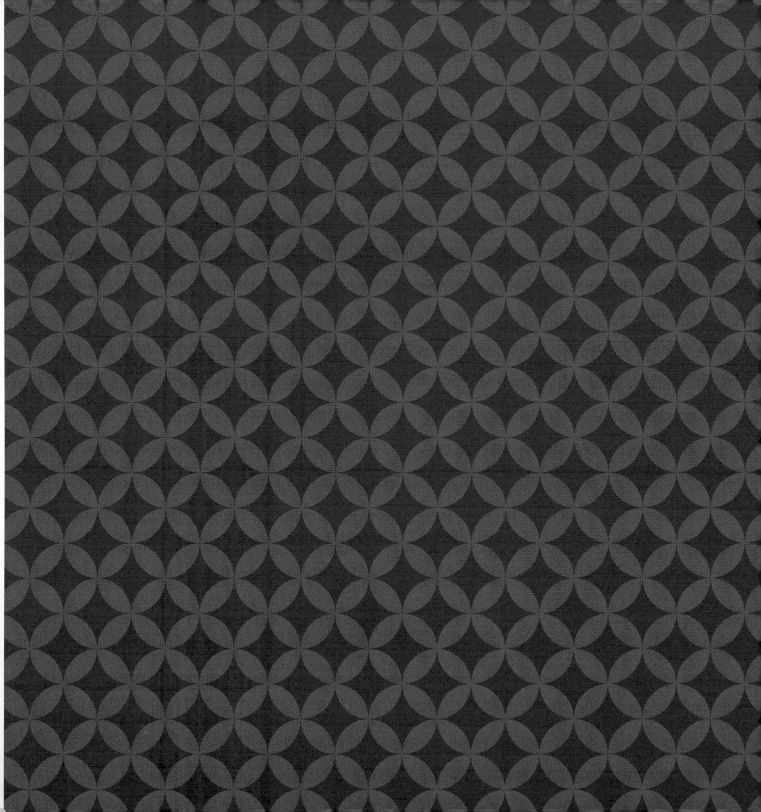

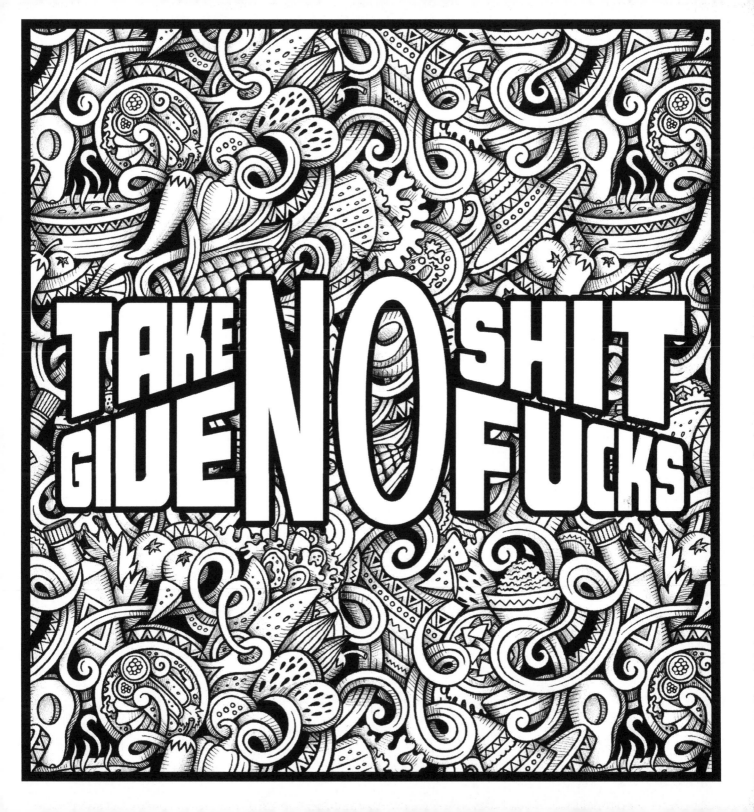

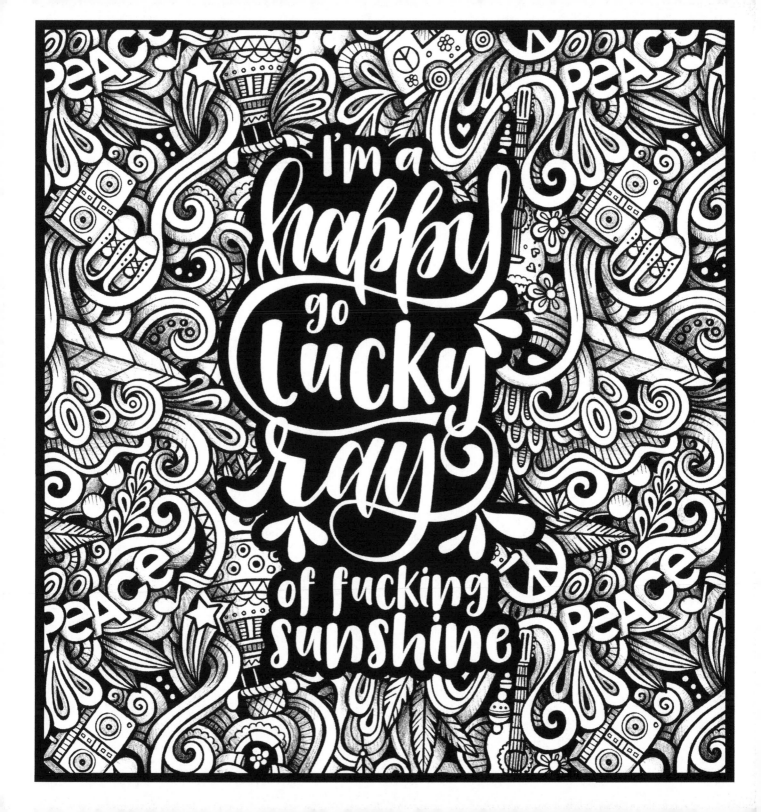

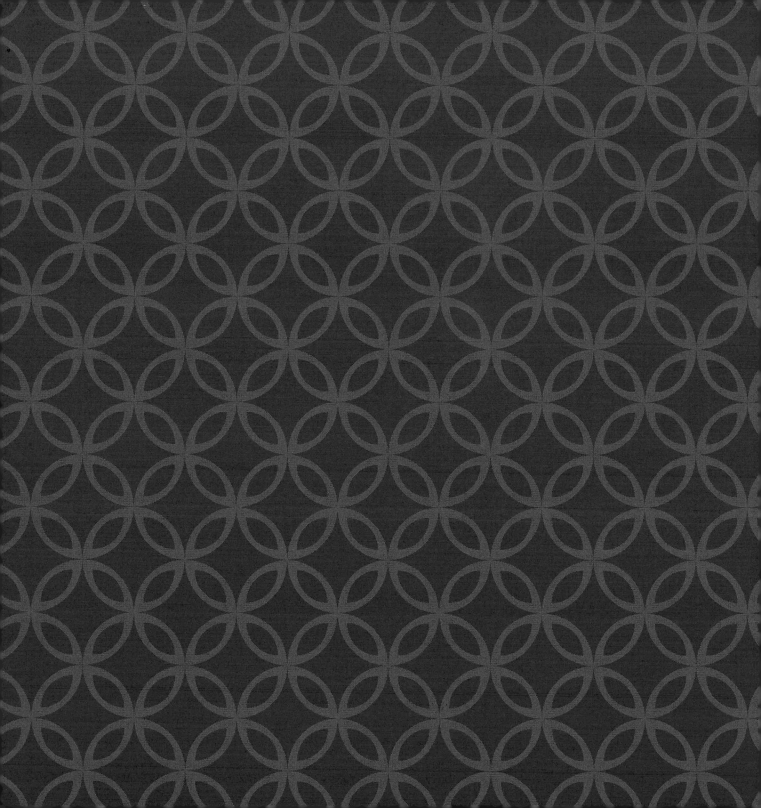

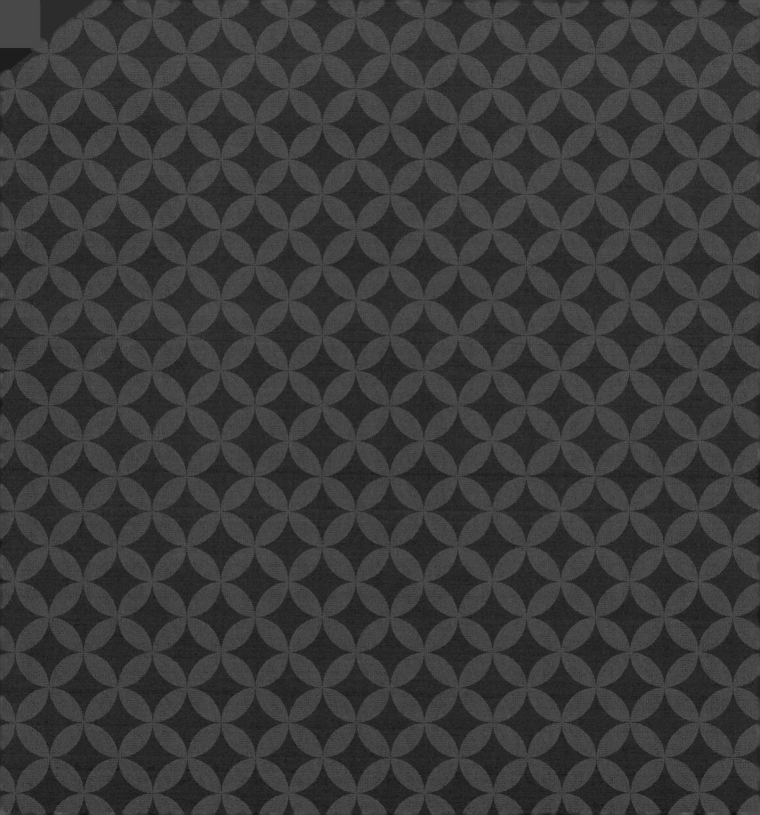

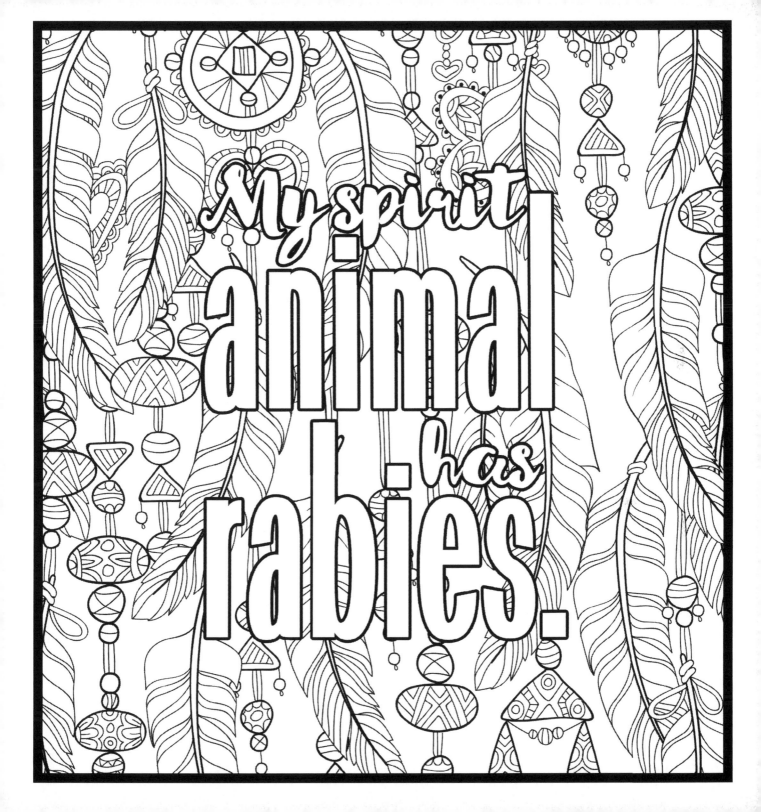

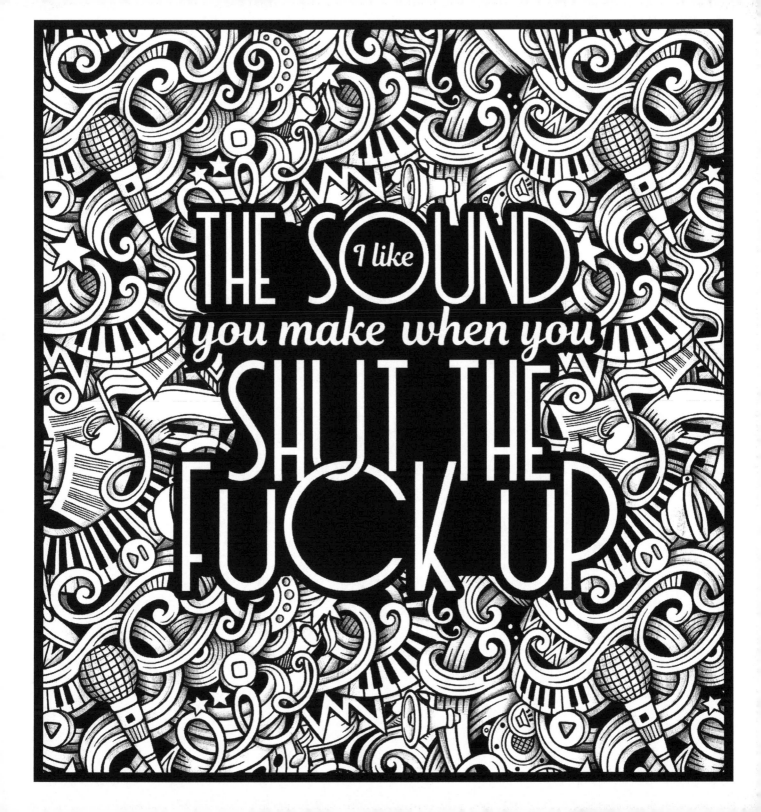

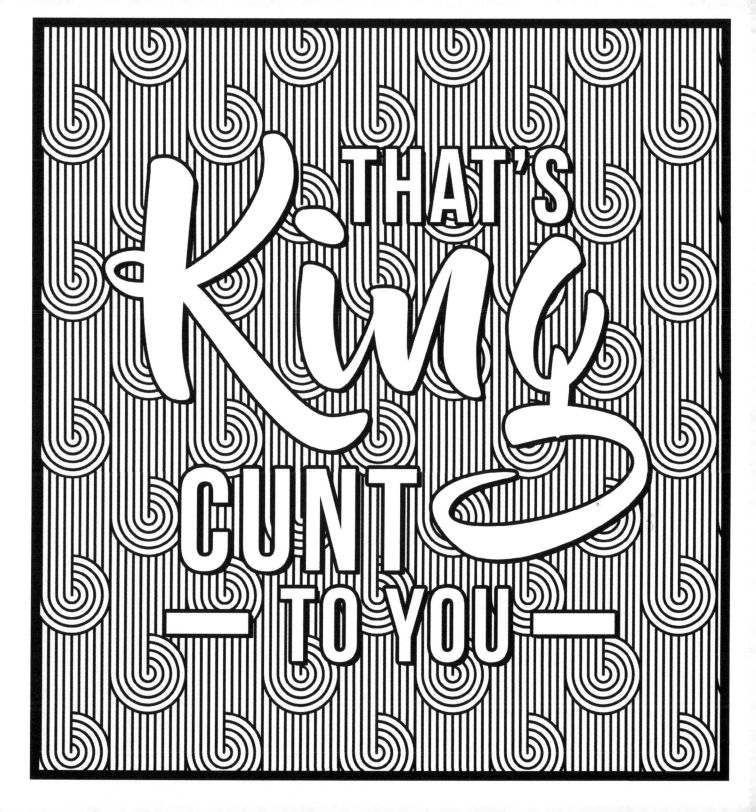

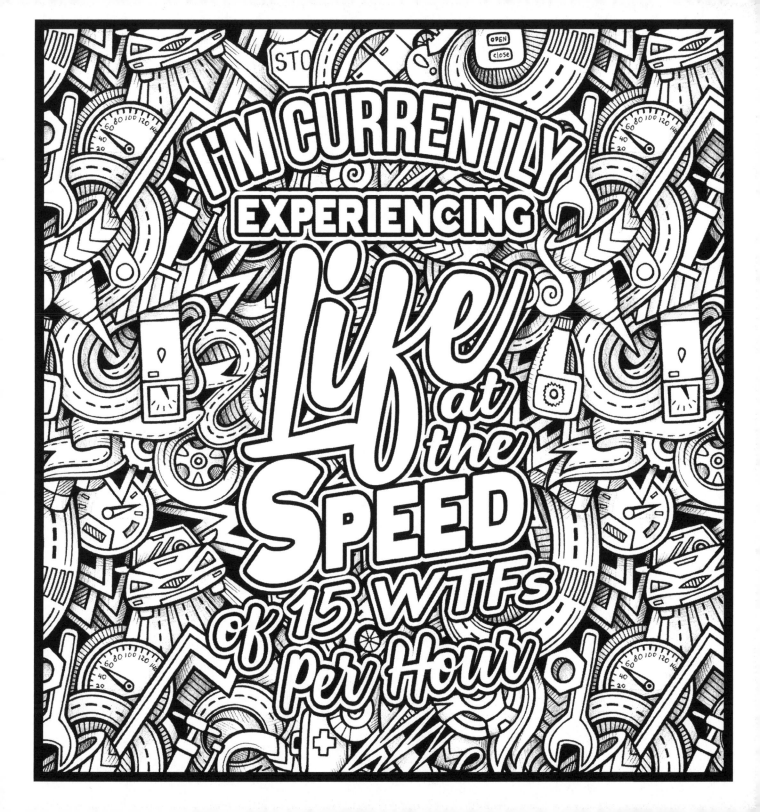

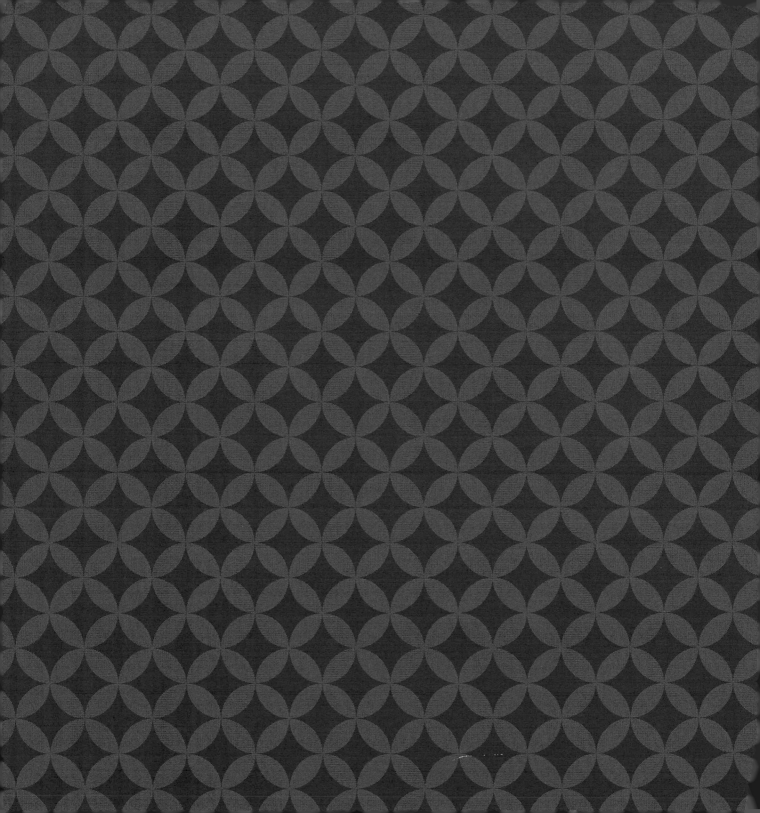

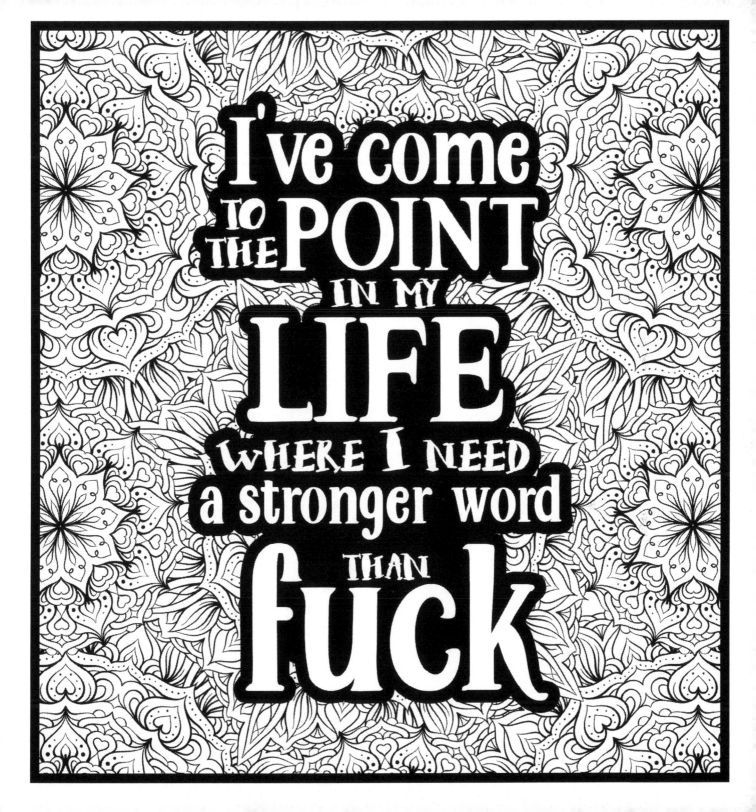

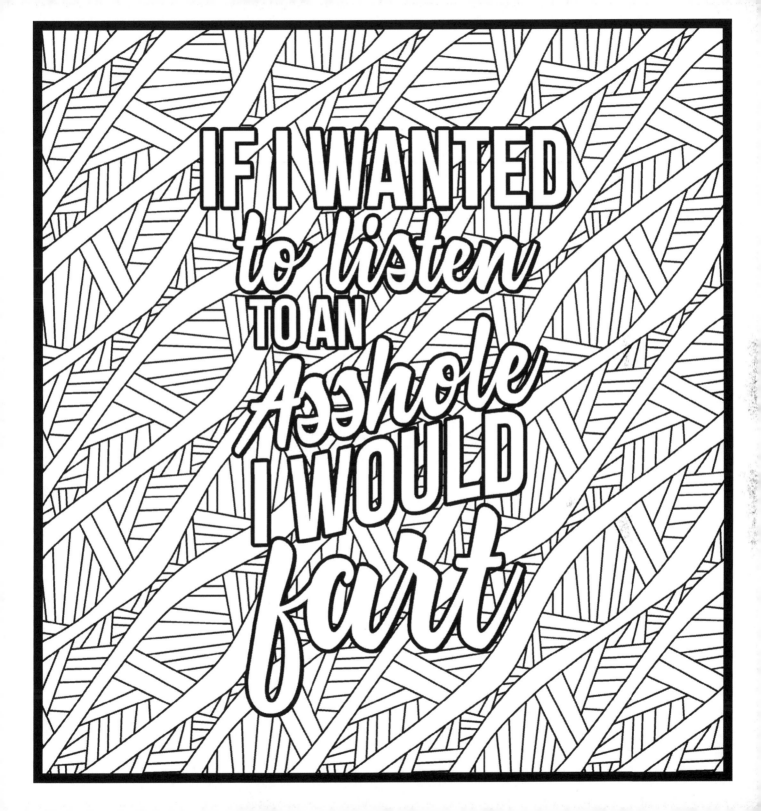

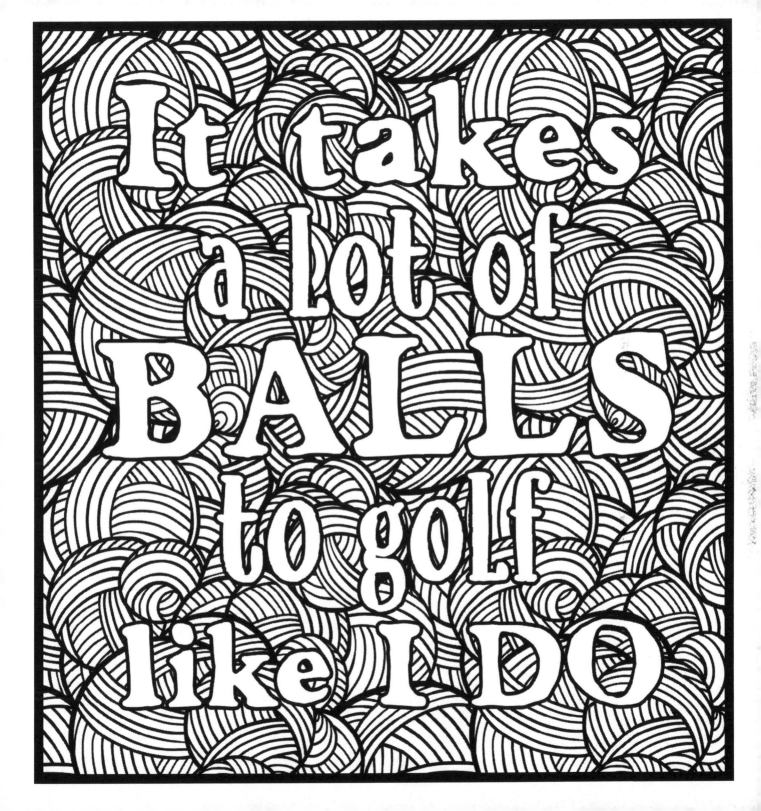

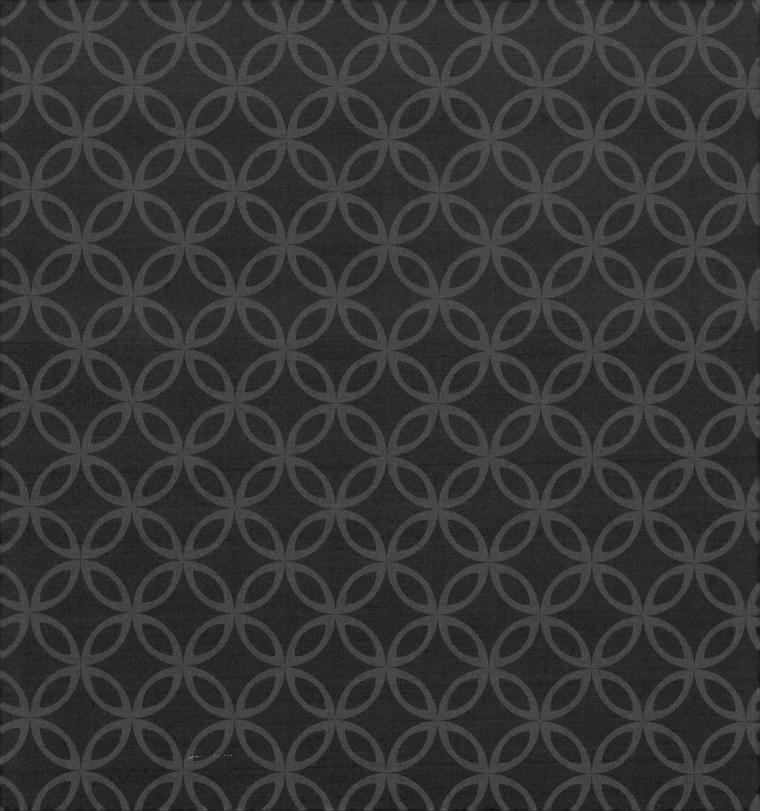

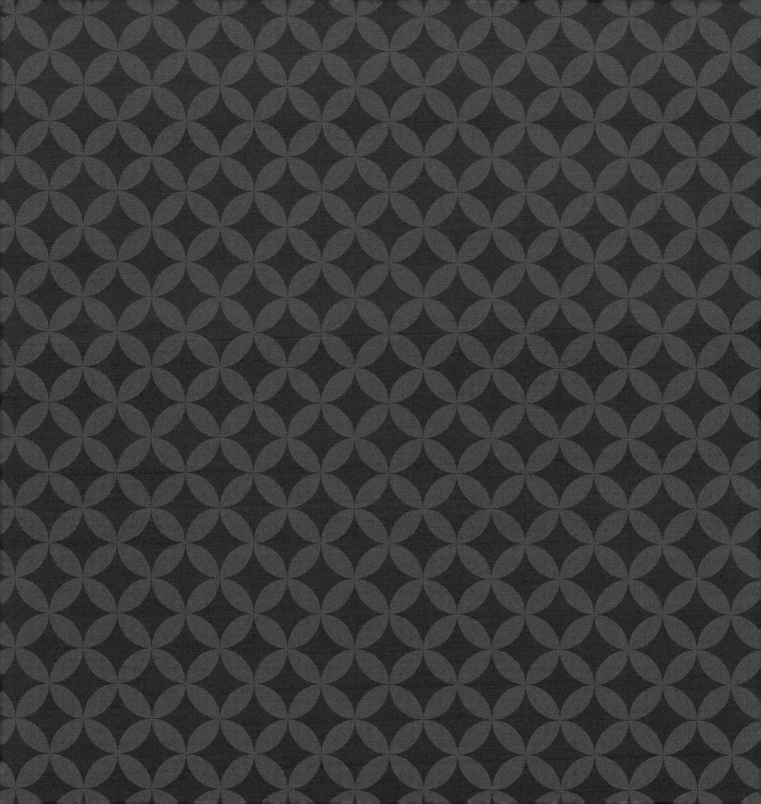

# FREE PDF DOWNLOAD
## OF THIS BOOK

**DOWNLOAD CODE:**

**DAD3963**

www.honeybadgercoloring.com/dadswears

Want free goodies?
Email us at freebies@honeybadgercoloring.com

@honeybadgercoloring

Honey Badger Coloring

Shop our other books at
www.honeybadgercoloring.com

Wholesale distribution through Ingram Content Group
www.ingramcontent.com/publishers/distribution/wholesale

For questions and customer service, email us at
support@honeybadgercoloring.com

Made in the
USA
Middletown, DE